We Woof You From The Bottom Of Our Hearts.

Dedicated to my lovely family,
Especially my beautiful daughter Sophia and my amazing son Elias.
I love seeing the friendship and bond between a big sister and a little
brother and of course our pups Bella and Lady too.

Our crazy adventures are the inspiration behind this book,
may they always be crazy and exciting!!
Love mom

Welcome home I've been waiting for you for almost a year,
Bella and I are excited you're here.
So many adventures we have planned for you,
I have a list of all the things, we're going to do.
We woof you, from the bottom of our hearts!

Hooray Hooray I'm a big sister today,
together we will always play.
This is how you build with blocks,
and this is how you make puppets out of socks.
We woof you, from the bottom of our hearts!

I want to be the best big sister,
I'll love you forever little mister.
As the best big sister, I'll give you ice cream.
I'm sure together we will be the greatest team.
We woof you, from the bottom of our hearts!

We can play tag or hide and seek,
let's stay quiet, shhh don't speak.
Bella can try and find us,
I hope she doesn't make a fuss.
We woof you, from the bottom of our hearts!

Swimming in the pool is so much fun,

I know you will love the summer sun.

Let's go through the sprinklers and down the slide too,

we're having so much fun, who knew.

We woof you, from the bottom of our hearts!

Beach days are the best days,
building sand castles and soaking in some rays.
It's so much fun getting buried in the sand,
or laying on the towel, I love getting tanned.
We woof you, from the bottom of our hearts!

As we get older we like different things,
a new adventure begins.
You like soccer and I like cheer,
We will always support each other, that is clear.
We woof you, from the bottom of our hearts!

We love the fall, one of our favorite seasons,
here are a few of our many reasons.
Apple picking, pumpkin picking,
let's not forget trick or treating.
But most important it's your birthday too,
you're turning three now, oh! how you grew.
We woof you, from the bottom of our hearts!

A few months later and it's spring,
with visits to the Easter bunny,
and baskets for the egg hunts don't forget to bring.
It's almost my birthday hooray,
I can't wait with you to celebrate the day.
We woof you, from the bottom of our hearts!

Our adventure packed weekends,
Hiking in the mountains and going to Greenport the east end.
Amazing getaways like Memorial Day, Fourth of July and Labor Day,
Enjoying the carousel and the beautiful bay.
We woof you, from the bottom of our hearts!

We want to welcome Lady to our family,
our newest puppy and Bella living happily.
Let's take Lady on her first adventure of many,
snow sledding down the hill a plenty.
We woof her, from the bottom of our hearts!

Made in the USA
Middletown, DE
16 June 2024